WOLFGANG AMADEUS MOZART

DIE ZAUBERFLÖTE
THE MAGIC FLUTE

Overture to the Opera
K 620

Edited by/Herausgegeben von
Hermann Abert

Ernst Eulenburg Ltd
London · Mainz · Madrid · New York · Paris · Tokyo · Toronto · Zürich

Die Zauberflöte

Ouverture

W. A. Mozart
1756 - 1791
Köchel No. 620

4

E. E. 3714. 4355

E. E. 3714. 4355

10

16

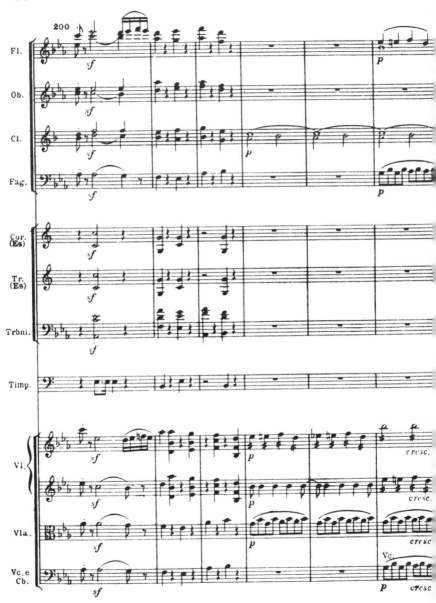